DISNEY

FROZEN II

Get Rid of the Dam!

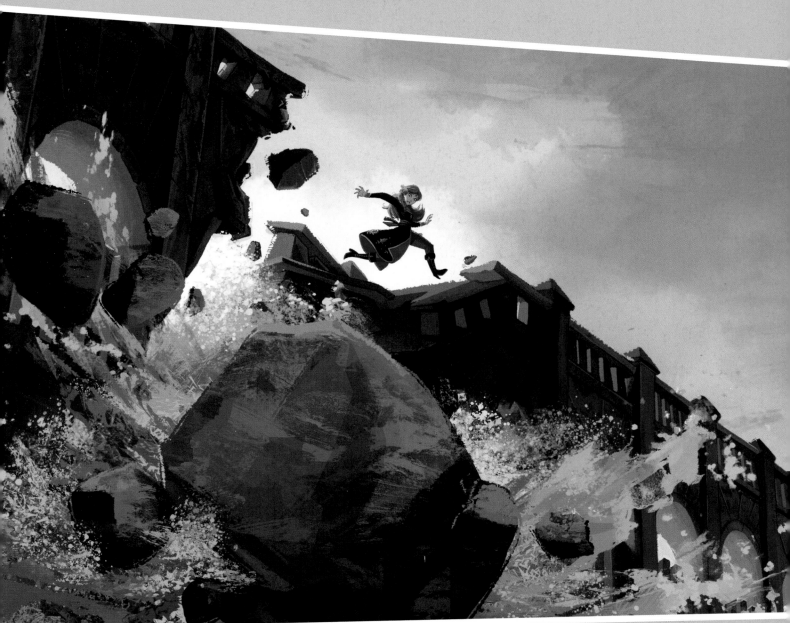

Adapted by Greg Cook

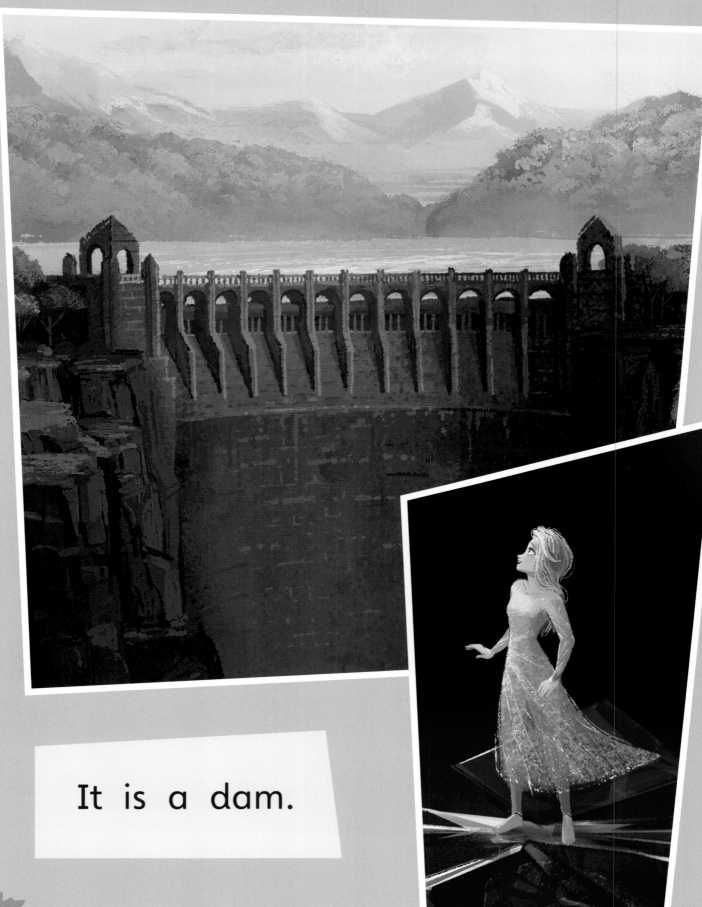

It is a dam.

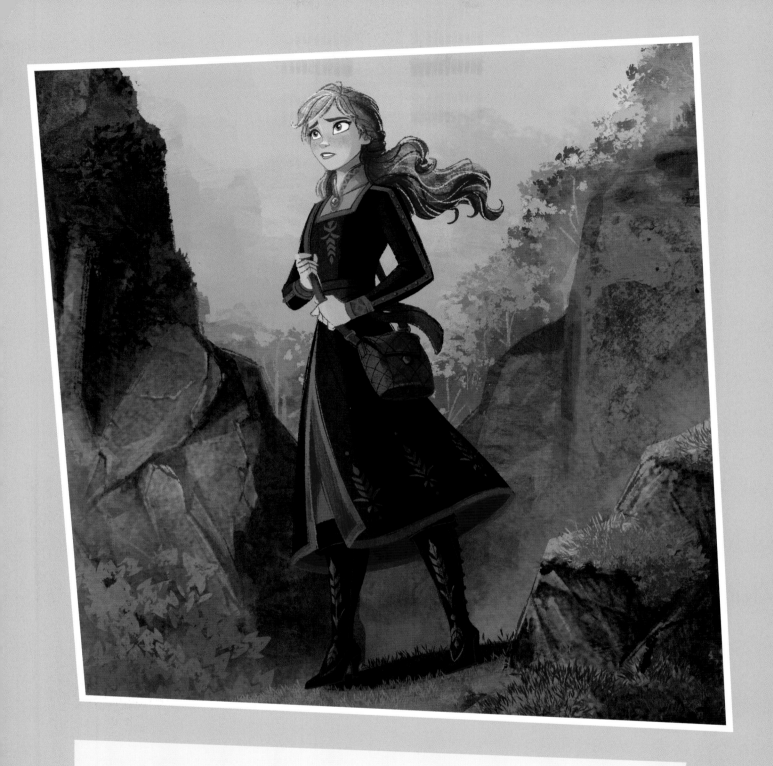

Go and get rid of the dam.

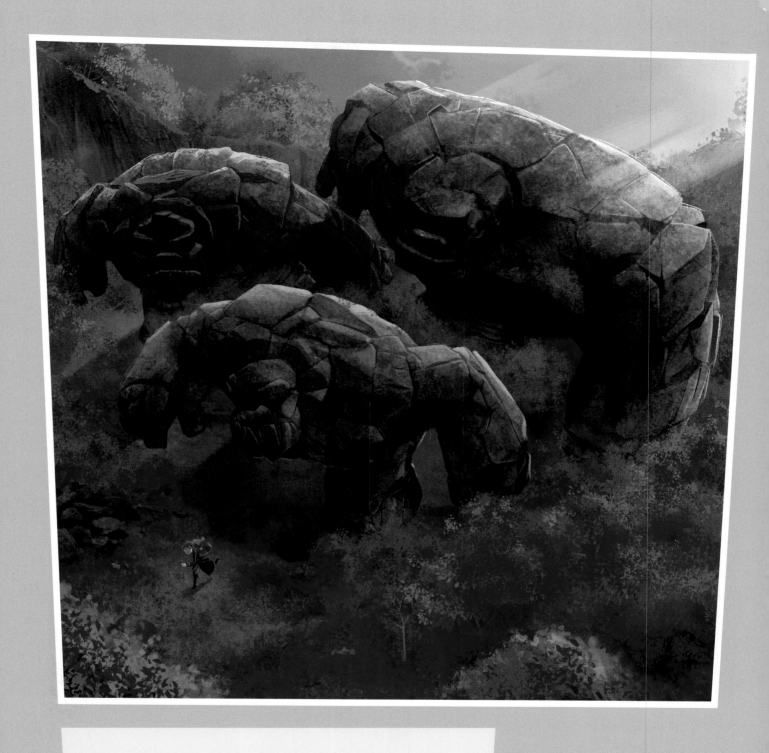

Get rocks!
Run to the dam.

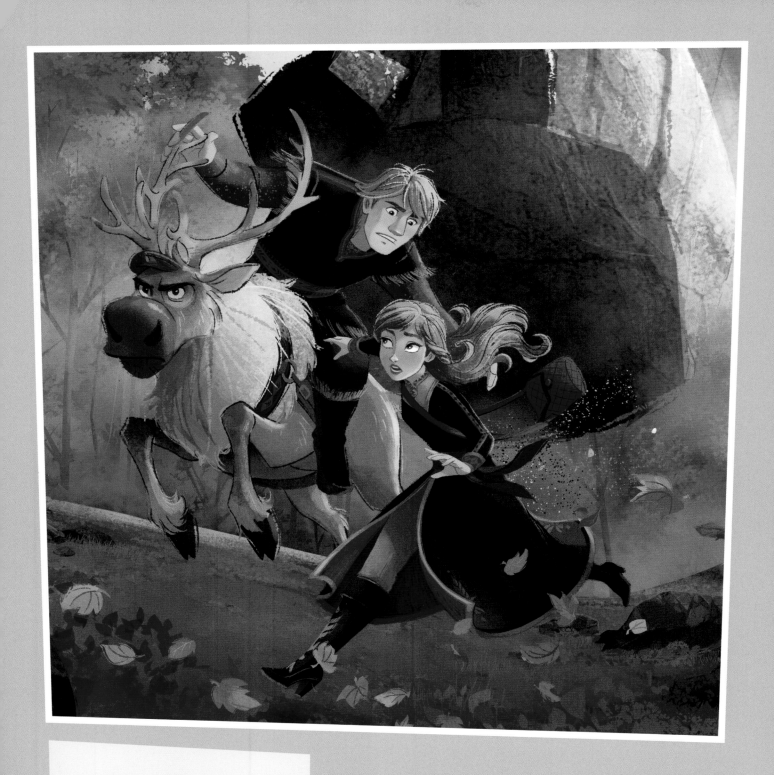

Get up!

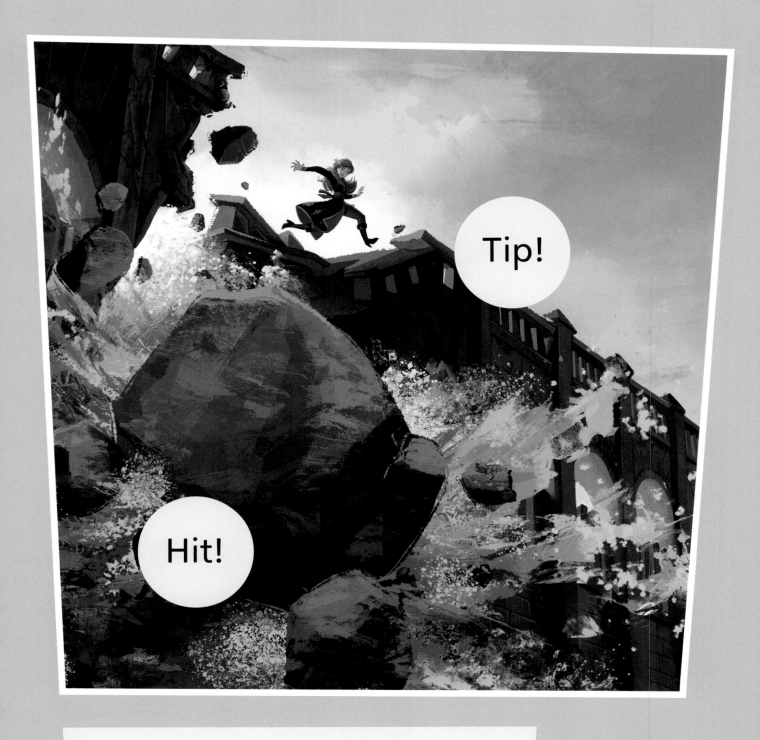

Get rid of the dam!
Tip in the rocks!

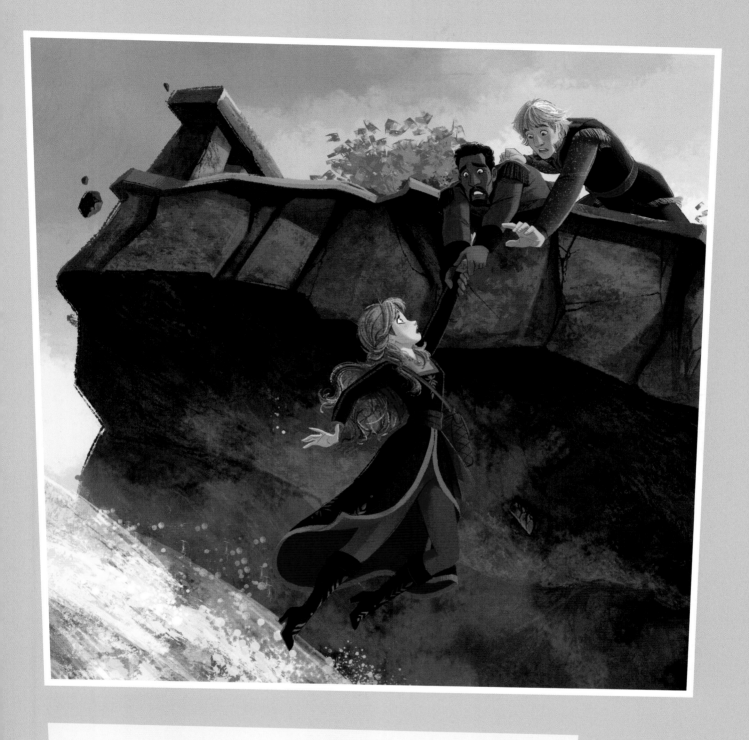

No! Get up to the top!

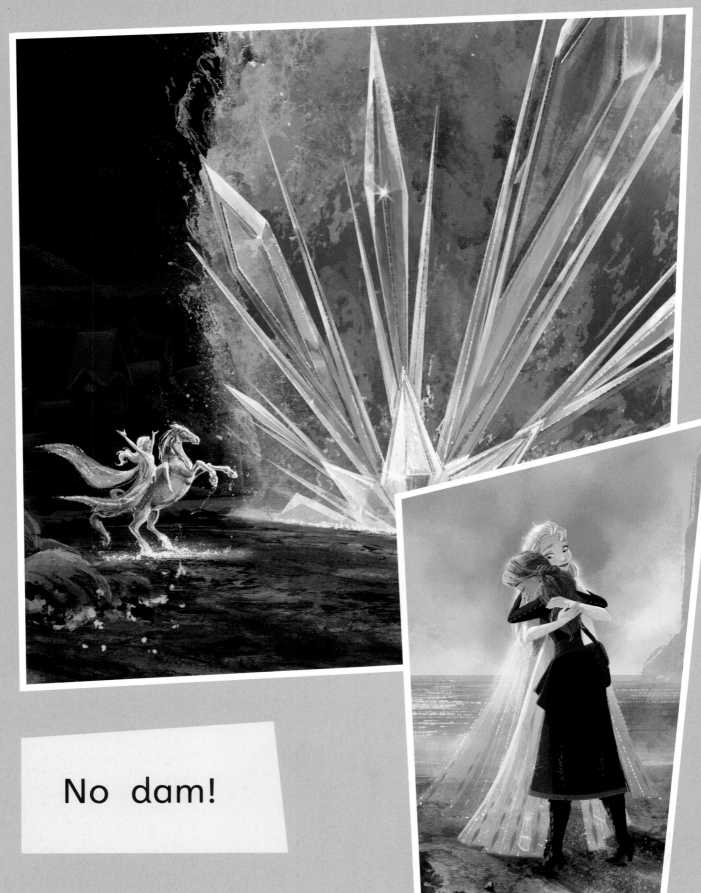

No dam!